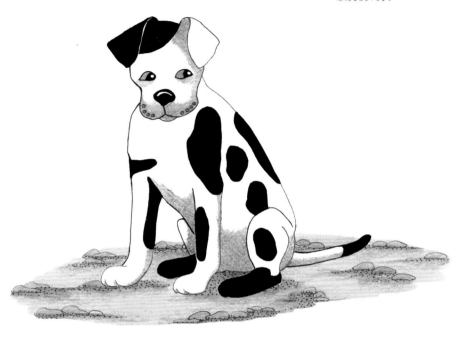

I am Sam.

I am a dog.

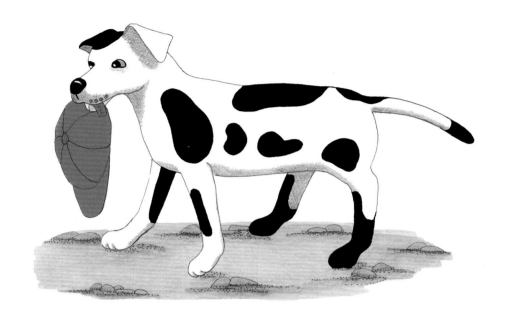

Sam has a red cap.

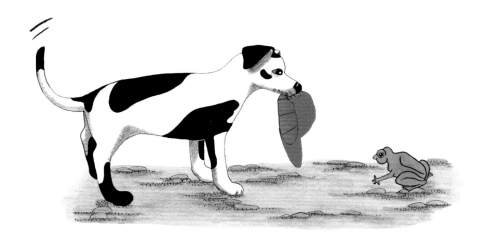

Sam can see a frog.

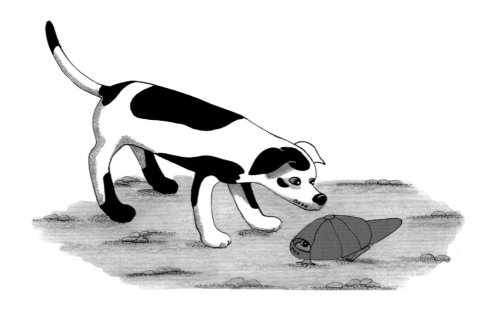

Sam put the red cap
on the frog.

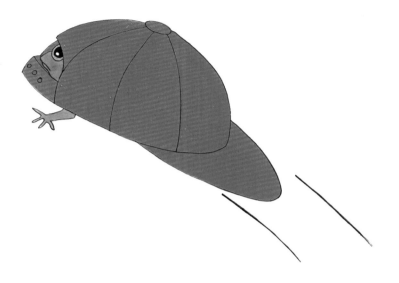

The frog hops.

The red cap hops.

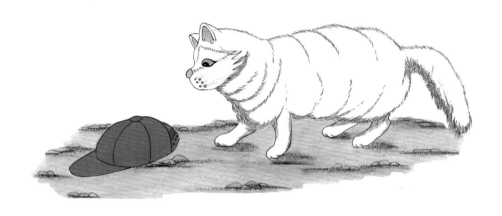

The fat cat can see
the red cap.

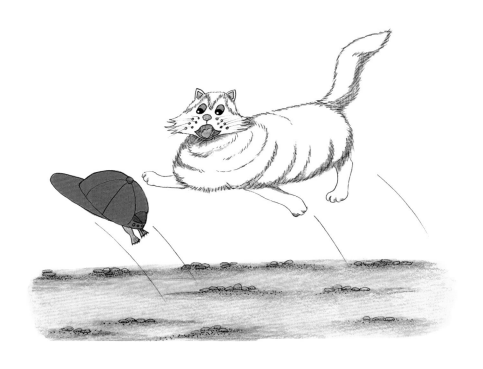

The frog hops.

The fat cat hops.

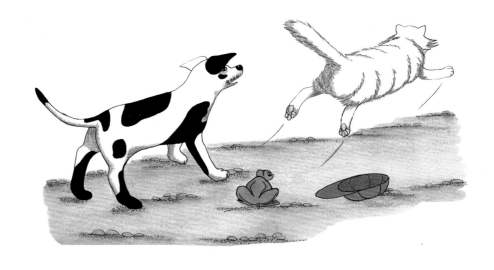

Sam and the frog
see the fat cat run
... and run ... and
run ...